Field Studies **6** (1986), 531–579

A KEY TO THE MAJOR GRO᾿
BRITISH FRESHWATER INVER᾿

by P. S. CROFT

Field Studies Council, Preston Montford, Montford Bridge, Shrewsbury SY4 1HW ᐟ

ABSTRACT

A key is provided to enable beginners to identify macroscopic (larger than 2 mm) British freshwater animals to their major group and, where possible, to family or species. It is intended for use with living material and makes appropriate use of behavioural characters, whilst providing a morphological backup. Like all other AIDGAP keys, an earlier version was tested extensively by school and university students: this, the first published edition, takes account of the resulting comments.

INTRODUCTION

This key was written to enable **beginners** to identify **living** animals encountered during field studies. There is, therefore, some emphasis on behavioural characters—which are often more useful than morphological ones. Morphological characters have been given, in each case, as an alternative; but there is no substitute for a healthy animal which can be returned to the water. If dead specimens are all that are available, they will, in most cases, key out without difficulty.

The key is designed to work with samples collected in a "standard" pond net and most animals less than 2 mm long have been omitted. Some groups (e.g. planktonic Crustacea)—which can be found in such quantities as to make this arbitrary guideline seem unreasonable—have been included, but it should be borne in mind that not all small animals are. All Protozoa, Rotifera and Nematoda are excluded on this basis.

The key covers the invertebrates found in all types of fresh water: pools, lakes, streams and rivers. It does not include the communities found in brackish water and should not be used in estuarine habitats.

In most cases the key will enable users to identify organisms down to family level but where it has not been found possible to discover characters that separate the different families within an order (or in some cases orders within a class, or even classes within a phylum) using a hand lens—then no separation has been attempted. The key was created for the interested beginner, not for the expert, and characters which require considerable expertise were avoided.

How to use the keys

Each key follows the traditional dichotomous form: that is, it consists of pairs of conflicting descriptions (couplets)—one of the pair matches the characteristics of the animal being identified, the other does not. All the user has to do is to choose the appropriate description and to follow the instruction given. This will either be a name, a number (which refers to a later couplet) or a name together with a reference to a later key. It is ESSENTIAL to read both parts of the couplet carefully before making the choice in order to avoid error: a wrong choice leads the user into the "wrong" part of the key—correct identification is then impossible. The guide has been split into subsidiary keys to

*Present address: Shrewsbury College of Arts and Technology, London Road, Shrewsbury.

make it easier to use, and to allow entry at a later stage if the user is confident that partial identification can be made without reference to the earlier keys.

The inexperienced are recommended to start at the beginning until they are familiar with representatives of most major groups. A hand lens will be needed for some of the characters. If access to a low-powered (× 20) binocular microscope can be arranged this will be very helpful, but not essential, as the key was designed to be used in the field as well as indoors.

Note: If, despite using all the relevant keys, you still cannot identify a specimen, as a last resort you could take it (by appointment) to the British Museum (Natural History) in London—or send it there by post—but it is important that we do not abuse this invaluable public service.

Diagrams and glossary

The illustrations are an integral part of the guide and are referred to as Fig. 1, Fig. 2, and so on. Note that the numbering of couplets and figures in each key starts at 1. Care has been taken to avoid specialist terminology whenever possible, but where this has proved unavoidable the appropriate illustration has been labelled to avoid confusion. Arrows have been used to highlight some of the features used for identification. Be aware that only a minute proportion of British freshwater animals have been illustrated, and identified specimens may differ from those examples drawn. However, if the animal to be identified and the illustrated specimen contrast considerably (particularly in the characters used for identification) then the authenticity of the identification should be checked. Similarly, it can be misleading to use diagrams alone for identification: stream animals in particular have often evolved similar characteristics to cope with the water current and can appear identical if only examined superficially.

A Glossary has been included on p. 578, and should be referred to whenever necessary.

Taxonomy

The taxonomy and nomenclature follow Maitland (1977), *A Coded Checklist of Animals occurring in Fresh Water in the British Isles,* published by the Institute of Terrestrial Ecology. It seemed sensible to use a single source for names. The animal kingdom is divided into a number of **Phyla** (singular Phylum), for example the Phylum Arthropoda. Each Phylum is divided in turn into a number of **Classes;** each Class into **Orders;** each Order into **Families;** each Family into **Genera** and each Genus into **Species.** The generic and specific names are conventionally printed in italics. Colloquial names are given where possible but users should be aware that they are not always very helpful. Such names are frequently local in usage and often one common name refers to many different species, or even to a whole phylum. As long as they are used with care, with their accompanying scientific name, they can be useful as an "aide memoire".

ACKNOWLEDGEMENTS

This key was conceived out of necessity many years ago and has undergone a long period of gestation. During this time, several versions have been thoroughly tested (in at least two languages). Anne Bebbington, Steve Tilling and John Crothers have proved admirable "midwives" during the long and difficult birth. Several "generations" of FSC staff have used the key and made their contributions to its final form. Henry Disney deserves special mention in this context. The greatest stimulus, however, has been that from students and teachers visiting the Field Centres: their support has been invaluable.

The single most important improvement in recent years occurred when Marilyn Crothers agreed to illustrate the key. Grateful acknowledgement is also made to the Burke Publishing Company for permission to reproduce a number of drawings from *The Young Specialist looks at Pond Life.*

BIBLIOGRAPHY

ENGLEHARDT, Wolfgang (1964: 1973). *The young specialist looks at Pond Life.* Burke Books.

FITTER, R. and MANUEL, R. (1986). *Field Guide to the Freshwater Life of Britain and North West Europe.* Collins, London.

MACAN, T. T. (1959). *A guide to Freshwater Invertebrate Animals.* Longman.

READER'S DIGEST ASSOCIATION LTD (1984). *Field Guide to the Water Life of Britain.* Reader's Digest.

Worms

BALL, Ian R. & REYNOLDSON, T. B. (1981). *British Planarians.* Synopses of the British Fauna (New Series) No. 19. Published for the Linnean Society of London and the Estuarine and Brackish Water Sciences Association by Cambridge University Press.

BRINKHURST, R. O. (1963). *A guide for the identification of British aquatic Oligochaeta.* Freshwater Biological Association Scientific Publication No. 22.

ELLIOTT, J. M. & MANN, K. H. (1979). *A key to the British Freshwater Leeches, with notes on their life cycles and ecology.* Freshwater Biological Association Scientific Publication No. 40.

REYNOLDSON, T. B. (1978). *A key to the British species of Freshwater Triclads (Turbellaria, Paludicola).* Freshwater Biological Association Scientific Publication No. 23.

Insects

AGUILAR, J., DOMMANGET, J.-L., and PRÉCHAC. (1986). *A field guide to the Dragonflies of Britain, Europe and North Africa.* Collins, London.

CRANSTON, P. S. (1982). A key to the larvae of the British Orthocladiinae (Chironomidae). Freshwater Biological Association Scientific Publication No. 45.

DAVIES, L. (1968). *A key to the British species of Simuliidae (Diptera) in the larval, pupal and adult stages.* Freshwater Biological Association Scientific Publication No. 24.

DISNEY, R. H. L. (1975). *A key to the larvae, pupae and adults of the British Dixidae (Diptera).* Freshwater Biological Association Scientific Publication No. 31.

EDINGTON, J. M. & HILDREW, A. G. (1981). *A key to the Caseless Caddis Larvae of the British Isles, with notes on their ecology.* Freshwater Biological Association Scientific Publication No. 43.

ELLIOTT, J. M. (1977). *A key to the larvae and adults of British freshwater Megaloptera and Neuroptera.* Freshwater Biological Association Scientific Publication No. 35.

FRIDAY, LAURIE E. (1986). A key to the adults of British Water Beetles. AIDGAP Test Version.

GIBBONS, Bob. (1986). *Dragonflies and Damselflies of Britain and Northern Europe.* Country Life Guides, Hamlyn, London.

HAMMOND, Cyril O. [revised by Robert Merritt] (1983). *The dragonflies of Great Britain and Ireland*, with enlarged colour illustrations of the British species by the late C. O. Hammond and an illustrated key to the aquatic larval stages by the late A. E. Gardner. Harley Books.

HICKEN, N. E. (1967). *Caddis Larvae. Larvae of the British Trichoptera.* Hutchinson, London.

MACAN, T. T. (1965). *A revised key to the British Water Bugs (Hemiptera–Heteroptera) with notes on their ecology.* Freshwater Biological Association Scientific Publication No. 16.

MACAN, T. T. (1961: 1979). *A key to the Nymphs of the British Species of Ephemeroptera, with notes on their ecology.* Freshwater Biological Association Scientific Publication No. 20.

McGEERY, Andrew (1986). *A complete guide to British Dragonflies.* Jonathan Cape, London.

HYNES, H. B. N. (1977). *A key to the adults and nymphs of the British Stoneflies (Plecoptera) with notes on their ecology and distribution.* Freshwater Biological Association Scientific Publication No. 17.

Crustacea

GLEDHILL, T., SUTCLIFFE, D. W. & WILLIAMS, W. D. (1976). *A key to the British Freshwater Crustacea: Malacostraca.* Freshwater Biological Association Scientific Publication No. 32.

GODDARD, J. S. & HOGGER, J. B. (1986). The current status and distribution of freshwater crayfish in Britain. *Field Studies,* 6, 383–396.

HARDING, J. P. & SMITH, W. A. (1974). *A key to the British freshwater Cyclopid and Calanoid Copepods.* Freshwater Biological Association Scientific Publication No. 18.

SCOURFIELD, D. J. & HARDING, J. P. (1966). *A key to the British species of Freshwater Cladocera.* Freshwater Biological Association Scientific Publication No. 5.

Molluscs

ELLIS, A. E. (1978). *British Freshwater Bivalve Mollusca.* Synopsis of the British Fauna No. 11, published for the Linnean Society of London by Academic Press.

FRETTER, V. & GRAHAM, A. (1978). The Prosobranch Molluscs of Britain and Denmark. Part 3, Neritacea, Viviparacea, Valvatacea, terrestrial and freshwater Littorinacea and Rissoacea. Published as supplements to *The Journal of Molluscan Studies.*

MACAN, T. T. & COOPER, R. D. (1949: 1960). *A key to the British Fresh and Brackish Water Gastropods.* Freshwater Biological Association Scientific Publication No. 13.

Bryozoa

MUNDY, S. P. (1980). *A key to the British and European Freshwater Bryozoans.* Freshwater Biological Association Scientific Publication No. 41.

KEY ONE: KEY TO THE MAJOR GROUPS OF FRESHWATER
INVERTEBRATES

The scale lines included with the illustrations indicate the actual size of large full-grown individuals. Your specimen may be smaller

1   Animal living in a shell, case or tube (Figs 1–3) 2

—   Animal free-living (without a shell, case or tube) 5

2   Animal living in a case or tube which it has constructed from silk, sand, stones or vegetation (Fig. 3) . Phylum ARTHROPODA, Class Insecta
                                                             insect KEY 2
                                                               (p. 542)

—   Animal with a true shell (Figs 1 and 2) 3

3   "Shell" is in fact the hardened exoskeleton of a crustacean (Fig. 4)
        . . . . . Phylum ARTHROPODA, Class Crustacea **crustacean** KEY 4
                                                                (p. 552)

—   Shell is a true molluscan shell into which the soft body can be retracted (Figs 1 and 2) 4

4   Shell consists of two matching parts (Fig. 1)
        . . . . Phylum MOLLUSCA, Class Bivalvia **bivalve** KEY 5
                                                                (p. 556)

—   Shell is in one piece, though there may be a door or plate which closes the opening (Fig. 2) . . Phylum MOLLUSCA, Class Gastropoda **snail** KEY 6
                                                                 (p. 558)

5   Animal with three or more pairs of true jointed legs (Figs 4–7) (those with apparently one or two such pairs have three if examined closely—or the specimen is damaged). 6

—   Animal with no true jointed legs (although it may have false legs or prolegs—see Fig 13) 11

6   Animal with three pairs of jointed legs (may appear to have only one or two pairs unless examined closely) (Fig. 5)
        . . . . Phylum ARTHROPODA, Class Insecta **insect** KEY 2
                                                                (p. 542)

—   Animal with four or more pairs of jointed legs (Figs 4, 6 and 7) 7

7   Animal with four pairs of jointed legs (Figs 6 and 7). 8

—   Animal with more than four pairs of jointed legs (Figs 4 and 8) 10

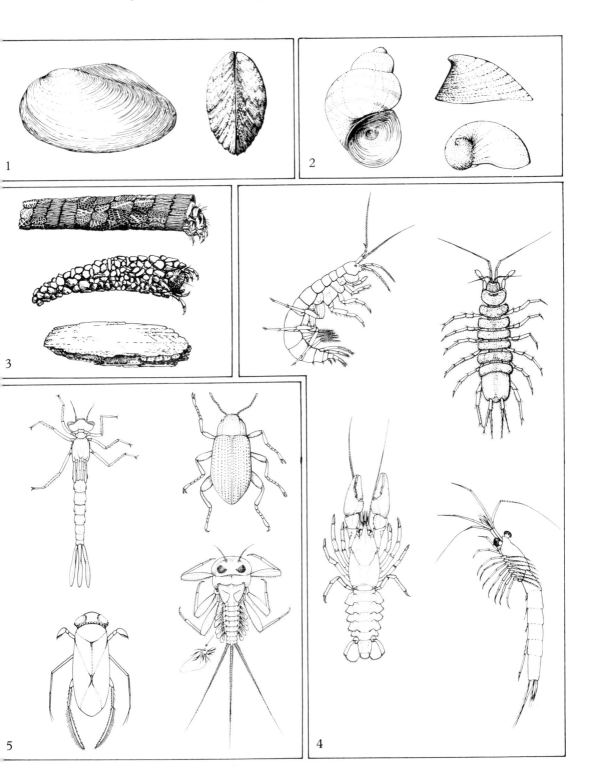

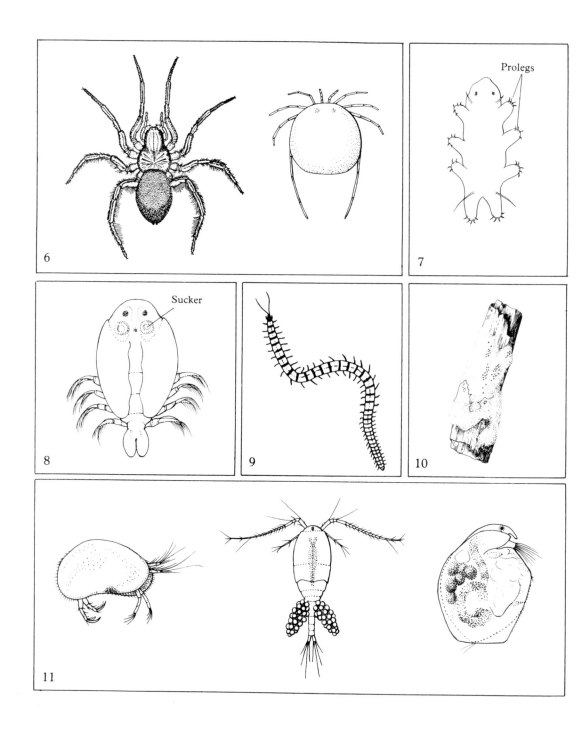

8   Animal with four pairs of true jointed legs (Fig. 6); may be small or
     large 9

—   Animal of distinctive shape (Fig. 7). When examined closely it is seen to
     possess clawed, unjointed prolegs. Small (less than 2 mm) and often
     found in damp moss etc. . . . . . . Phylum TARDIGRADA   **water bear**

9   Animal oval in shape with two suckers under the thorax (Fig. 8)
     . . . . . Phylum ARTHROPODA, Class Crustacea   **crustacean**   KEY 4
                                                                        (p. 553)

—   Animal without suckers (Fig. 6)
     . . . . .   Phylum ARTHROPODA, Class Arachnida   **arachnid**   KEY 3
                                                                        (p. 550)

10   Animal with the main part of its body composed of about 50 segments
     each of which bears a pair of walking legs (Fig. 9)
     . . Phylum ARTHROPODA, Class Chilopoda, Order Geophilomorpha, family
                                    Geophilidae ***Strigamia maritima***
                        a marine centipede reported from freshwater in 1982

—   Number of body segments bearing walking (or swimming) legs is less
     than 10 (Fig. 4)
     . . . . . Phylum ARTHROPODA, Class Crustacea   **crustacean**   KEY 4
                                                                        (p. 552)

11   Animal a "furry" encrustation, usually on the underside of a stone or stick
     (Fig. 10), or an erect twig-like structure; surface dotted with irregular
     pores. Incapable of movements visible to the naked eye
     . . . . Phylum PORIFERA   **sponge**

—   Animal not encrusting, though it may be attached to the substrate, and
     without irregular pores on its surface (Figs 11 onwards) 12

12   Animal small (less than 2 mm) "flea-like" and usually swimming in mid-
     water. Close observation will reveal several pairs of jointed legs, partly—
     or wholly—obscured by the exoskeleton (Fig. 11)
     . . . . . . Phylum ARTHROPODA, Class Crustacea   **crustacean**   KEY 4
                                                                        (p. 552)

—   Truly without jointed legs (Figs 12 onwards) 13

13   Animal segmented. Segment junctions visible through a handlens (Figs
     12–15) 14

—   Animal unsegmented (Figs 16 onwards) 19

14   Thirteen or fewer segments (these are usually, but not always, at least as
      long as they are broad) 15

—   Fourteen or more segments (usually, but not always, broader than long) .   .   .17

15   Animal a fly chrysalis or pupa, contained in a brown or red pupal case
      (Fig. 12) .   .   .   .   . Phylum ARTHROPODA, Class Insecta   **insect**   KEY 2
                                                                                (p. 542)

—   Animal not in a brown or red pupal case 16

16   Front end equipped with a head capsule (pale brown head with jaws,
      antennae, eyes etc.) OR a pair of black biting jaws which can be seen
      inside the head of the maggot. (NB: the head is at the front end, don't be
      fooled by species that have false eyes at the rear end) (Fig. 13)
      .   .   .   . Phylum ARTHROPODA, Class Insecta   **insect**   KEY 2
                                                                                (p. 542)

—   Head without capsule or biting jaws, but it may (or may not) have a pair of
      simple eyespots 17

17   Animal with suckers at each end (not easy to see as they are underneath)
      with which it can attach, or move by looping (Fig. 14)
      .   .   .   . Phylum ANNELIDA, Class Hirudinea   **leech**   KEY 8
                                                                                (p. 564)

—   Animal without suckers (never loops, or attaches firmly to the substrate) .   .   .18

18   Maggot, with a pair of black jaws clearly visible inside the head when
      viewed through a lens (Fig. 13) (NB: the head is at the front end, don't be
      fooled by species that have false eyes at the rear end! These larvae appear
      to have more than 13 segments through "false segmentation")
      .   .   .   . .Phylum ARTHROPODA, Class Insecta   **insect**   KEY 2
                                                                                (p. 542)

—   Animal not maggot-like, jaws not visible inside the head; bristles may, or
      may not, be visible (Fig. 15)
      .   .   .   . .Phylum ANNELIDA, Class Oligochaeta   **true worm**

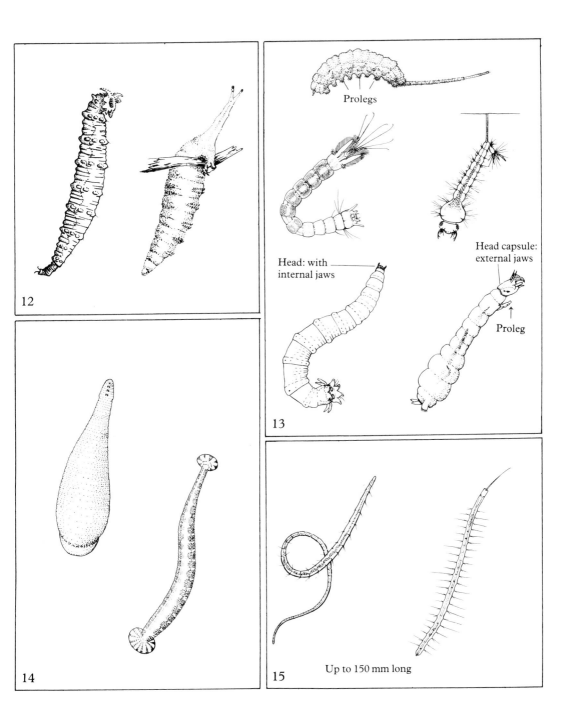

Prolegs

Head: with internal jaws

Head capsule: external jaws

Proleg

12

13

14

15

Up to 150 mm long

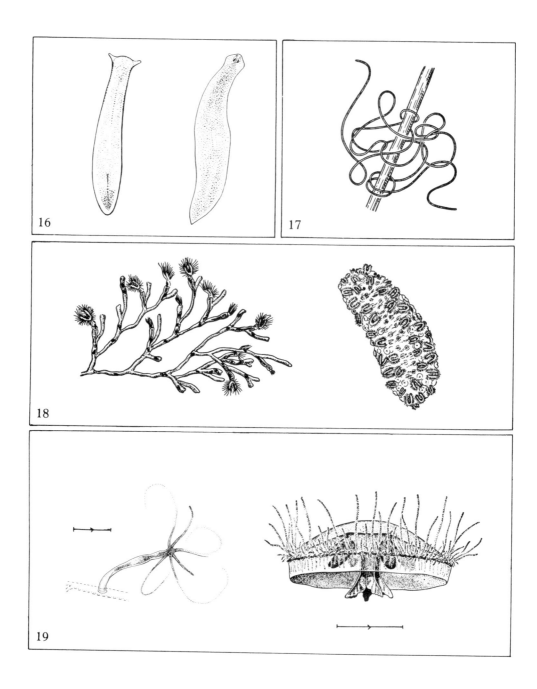

19   Animal with suckers at each end (not easy to see as they are underneath)
      with which it can attach or move by looping (Fig. 14) (animal is seg-
      mented, the segments are difficult to see)
      . . . .   Phylum ANNELIDA, Class Hirudinea   **leech**   KEY 8
                                                                        (p. 564)

—   Animal without suckers, may (or may not) attach firmly to the substrate,
      at the rear end (Figs 16 onwards) 20

20   Animal very flattened (less than 1 mm high), usually "gliding" over the
      substrate: either with one pair of easily seen eyespots, or with many eye-
      spots (which may be difficult to see on dark coloured animals) all round
      the edge of the front end (Fig. 16)
      . . . .Phylum PLATYHELMINTHES, Class Turbellaria Order Tricladida
                                                                flatworm

(**Note:** Very small flatworm-like organisms, also belonging to the Class Turbellaria—but to the Order
Microturbellaria—may key out here; but they are rounded not flattened)

—   Animal not flattened, not "gliding", and without eyespots 21

21   Animal a long (several centimetres) thin (1–2 mm diameter) black worm,
      looking like a hair from a horse's tail, feeling rough to the touch (Fig. 17).
      It coils and uncoils very slowly
      . . . .   Phylum NEMATOMORPHA, Class Gordioidea   **hairworm**

—   Animal unlike a hair from a horse's tail 22

22   A branching colony of tiny (1 mm) animalcules housed in transparent
      jelly or brownish tubes. Each animalcule is crowned by a horseshoe of
      tentacles which are retracted when disturbed (Fig. 18)
      . . . . Phylum POLYZOA   **moss animalcules**

—   Individual animals, not colonies, though some "budding" of up to three
      developing individuals may occur on the Polyp forms. Polyps resemble
      sea anemones, medusae resemble jellyfish (Fig. 19)
      . . . . .Phylum COELENTERATA, Class Hydrozoa "**Hydra**"'s and
                                                        freshwater jellyfish

KEY TWO: KEY TO THE ORDERS OF INSECTS found in freshwater
Phylum **Arthropoda,** Class **Insecta**

1   Animal living in a case or tube which it has constructed from silk, sand, stones, or vegetation (Fig. 1a) 2

—   Animal free-living (without a case or tube) 6

2   Animal with a case used as a mobile home which covers the abdomen; it may be sewn onto a rock or water plant. Do not remove the case 3

—   Animal in a long silk tube (often covered in silt, or fine particles of vegetation) attached to, or buried in, the substrate OR, in a case of leaf fragments, loosely sewn onto a plant leaf (Fig. 2). Remove the animal from its covering 4

3   Animal with jointed legs, which are used for walking or swimming; they are easily seen when the animal is moving, or by looking into the mouth of the case (Fig. 1a) OR animal in a case which has been closed up for pupation . . . . . . Order Trichoptera   **caddis larva** or **pupa** KEY 12 (p. 572)

—   Animal without jointed legs (carefully remove the case) (Fig. 3) . . . . .Order Diptera   **true fly larva** KEY 7 (p. 560)

4   Animal with a pair of hooks at the end of the abdomen (Fig. 1b) . . . . .Order Trichoptera   **caddis larva** KEY 12 (p. 572)

—   Animal without hooks (Figs 2 and 3) 5

5   Animal with three pairs of jointed legs, and four pairs of abdominal prolegs (Fig. 2)
    . . . Order Lepidoptera, family Pyralidae   **china mark moth caterpillar**

—   Animal without jointed legs, with prolegs at both front and rear ends (Fig. 3) . . . . .Order Diptera   **true fly larva** KEY 7 (p. 560)

6   Animal without jointed limbs; may or may not possess prolegs (Fig. 3) . . . 7

—   Animal with three pairs of jointed limbs (sometimes only one or two pairs are easily visible) (Fig. 4 onwards) 8

7   Infrequently encountered inhabitant of the air spaces within an aquatic plant, or living attached to a plant and piercing the air space with a tube at the rear end. Close examination will reveal rudimentary jointed limbs . . . . Order Coleoptera **beetle larva**

—   Animal without even rudimentary jointed limbs; most truly free living (Fig. 3), but a minority live in the air spaces, and some other species possess a tube at the rear end—though this is used to reach the water surface, not to pierce plant air spaces . Order Diptera   **true fly larva** KEY 7 (p. 560)

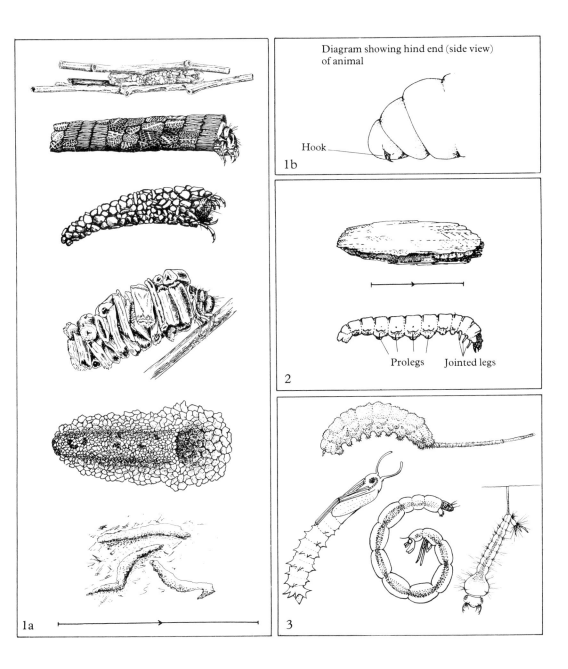

Diagram showing hind end (side view) of animal

Hook

1b

Prolegs   Jointed legs

2

1a

3

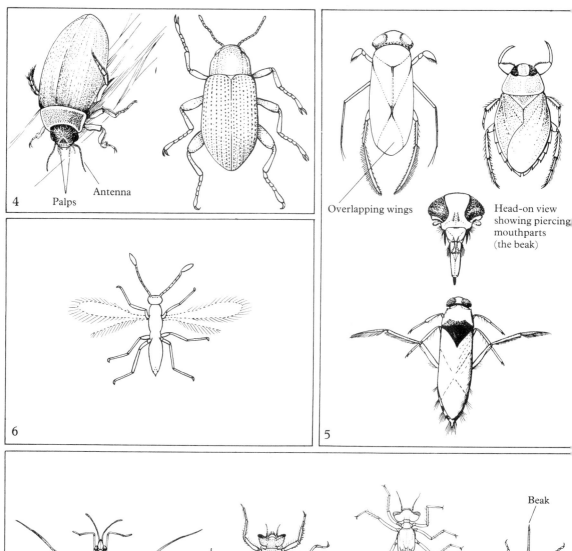

4 Palps   Antenna

Overlapping wings

Head-on view
showing piercing
mouthparts
(the beak)

6

5

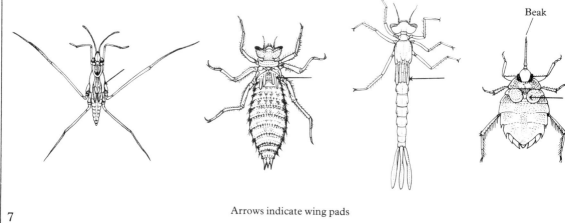

Beak

7   Arrows indicate wing pads

8   Animal an adult insect with fully developed wings. The first pair are
    often, but not always, modified to form hardened wing covers for the
    second pair. If you cannot see the abdominal segment junctions from
    above, they must be covered by wings, look for the join where the wings or
    wing cases meet or overlap (Figs 4, 5 and 6)   9

—   Animal without fully developed wings. It may, or may not, have wing
    pads (Fig. 7) but these will not cover more than half the abdominal
    segments 11

9   First pair of wings membranous (for flying), second pair forming a fringe
    of hairs. Tiny wasps about 1 mm long which may be found either on the
    surface or swimming underwater using their wings. Not common, but
    often in large numbers if they are found (Fig. 6)
    .   .   .   . Order Hymenoptera, family Chalcididae   **chalcid wasp**

—   First pair of wings modified to form covers for the second pair; these
    covers are horny and often match the rest of the exoskeleton (**beetles and
    bugs**) (Figs 4 and 5)   10

10 Wingcases overlap at the hind end; mouthparts may (or may not) be
    modified to form a piercing "beak" but never with segmented palps
    (Fig. 5)   .   .   .   . Order Hemiptera   **true bugs**   KEY 9
                                                                        (p. 566)

—   Wingcases meet down the midline of the back all the way down the
    abdomen; the mouthparts never form a piercing "beak" and always with
    segmented palps (Fig. 4).   .   .   .   . Order Coleoptera   **water beetles** KEY 10
                                                                        (p. 568)

11 Animal with between 1 and 5 "tails" (hairlike filaments, hooks or points)
    projecting from the end of the abdomen (Figs 8–18) 12

—   Animal without tails, hooks or points (Figs 19 onwards) (if you see two
    tufts of "hairs" here, look closely for hidden hooks (Fig. 11) 22

Note: Beware of "tail" breakages whilst working through the next few couplets; an animal with one tail in the
middle and another at one side of it was equipped with three before you collected it! Unbroken tail filaments
taper towards the ends. Also note that the last two pairs of abdominal gills should not be counted as tails when
an animal has several such pairs of gills.

12 Abdomen terminating in one tail (Figs 8, 9 and 10) (see note above) 13

—   Abdomen terminating in 2–5 "tails" (hairlike or leaflike filaments, hooks
    or tails) (Figs 11–18) (see note above) 15

13   Animal with gills all down the sides of the abdomen; usually backs away
     snapping its jaws if "attacked" by a pencil (Fig. 8)
     .   .   .   .   .Order Megaloptera, family Sialidae   **alderfly larva**

—   No abdominal gills; may, or may not, have spines protruding backwards
     from all segments 14

14   Front legs modified for grasping prey, mouthparts a beak, "tail" is an
     air breathing snorkel and can often be seen breaking the water surface
     (Fig. 9)   .   .   .   .   .Order Hemiptera   **true bug**   KEY 9
                                                                                (p. 566)

—   None of the above features; segment edges equipped with spines that
     overlay the next segment (Fig. 10)
     .   .   .   . Order Coleoptera, family Haliplidae   **beetle larva**

15   Animal with 2 or 4 "tails" (Figs 11–14) 16

—   Animal with 3 or 5 "tails" (Figs 15–18) 19

16   Tails terminating in tiny hooks, which may be partially hidden by tufts of
     hairs on the last two pairs of abdominal gills; the hooks can be used as
     grapples for moving backwards if the animal is disturbed (Figs 11 and 12)   .   . 17

—   Tails never terminating in hooks. The animal may, occasionally, move
     backwards but it cannot grapple without hooks (Figs 13 and 14) 18

17   Two hooks only (Fig. 11)   .   .   .   . Order Trichoptera   **caddis larva**   KEY 12
                                                                                (p. 573)

—   Four hooks (Fig. 12)
     .   .   .   .   .   . Order Coleoptera, family Gyrinidae   **whirlygig beetle larva**

18   Tails are segmented hairlike filaments (use a handlens), always at least
     one-third of the total head and body length (when complete). Most
     species found in clean streams and upland pools (Fig. 13)
     .   .   .   . Order Plecoptera   **stonefly nymph**

—   Tails are never segmented (use a lens), often less than one-third of total
     head and body length: they may, or may not, be breathing tubes to
     obtain air from the surface. Head characteristically rounded or pointed
     (Fig. 14)   .   .   .   . Order Coleoptera   **beetle larva**

19   "Tails" are just 3 or 5 short sharp points. Head characteristically angular
     when viewed from above, mouthparts in the form of a mask (Fig. 15).
     Animal may swim in jerks by pumping water at high pressure through the
     anus.   .   .   .   .   . Order Odonata, Sub-order Anisoptera   **dragonfly nymph**

—   Three tails, which may be hairlike filaments or flattened leaf-like struc-
     tures (caudal gills). Angular head and mask may, or may not, be present
     (Figs 16 and 17) 20

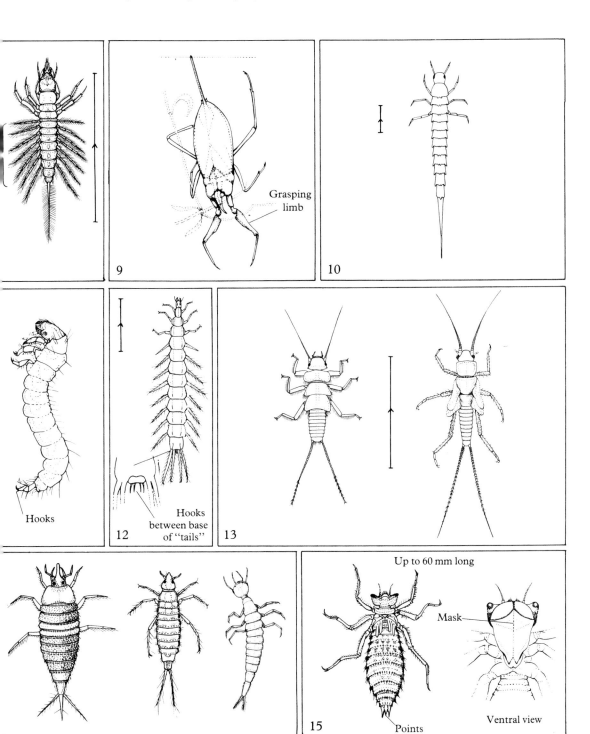

9

Grasping limb

10

Hooks

12

Hooks between base of "tails"   13

15   Points

Up to 60 mm long

Mask

Ventral view

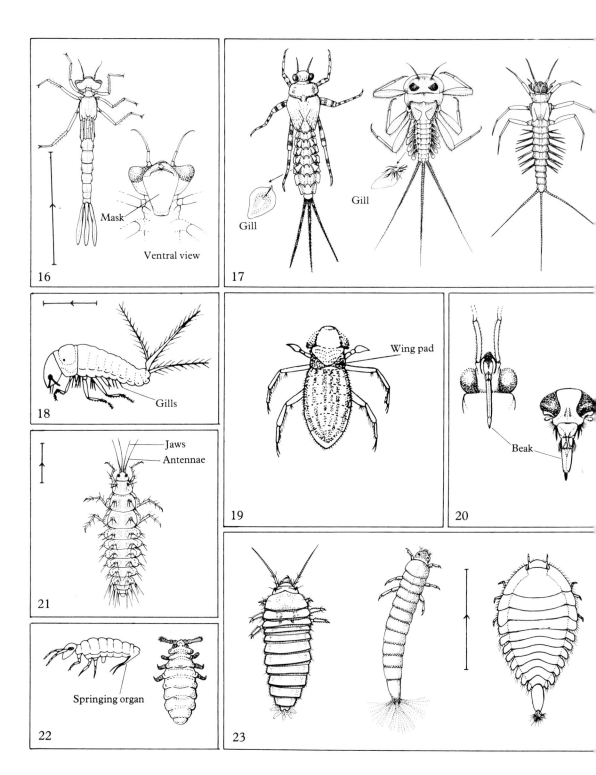

16   Mask   Ventral view

17   Gill   Gill

18   Gills

19   Wing pad

20   Beak

21   Jaws   Antennae

22   Springing organ

23

20   "Tails" flattened and leaf-like. Head angular, when viewed from above
      and the mouthparts form a mask. Most swim by moving the abdomen
      from side to side, a common species is green in colour (Fig. 16)
      . . . . Order Odonata, Sub-order Zygoptera   **damselfly nymph**

—   "Tails" hairlike filaments. Head usually rounded, mouthparts never a
      mask. Most swim by moving the abdomen up and down (Figs 17 and 18). . . 21

21   Abdominal gills present; these are attached to the sides, and most project
      laterally but in two families they are apparently dorsal and in one family
      they are partially hidden by covers (Fig. 17)
      . . . . Order Ephemeroptera   **mayfly nymph** KEY 11
                                                                          (p. 570)

—   Abdominal gills may, or may not, be present: if they are, they are ventral
      and cannot be seen from above (Fig. 18)
      . . . . Order Coleoptera   **water beetle larva**

22   Animal with at least one pair of legs elongated for rowing (Fig. 19)
      . . . . Order Hemiptera   **true bugs**   KEY 9
                                                                          (p. 566)

—   No pairs of legs modified for rowing 23

23   Mouthparts modified to form a single piercing "beak" (Fig. 20)
      . . . . Order Hemiptera   **true bugs**   KEY 9
                                                                          (p. 566)

—   Mouthparts not a single piercing "beak"   24

24   Mouthparts modified to form long slender tubes (Fig. 21); animal found
      living in a sponge, or amongst streamside vegetation (usually moss)
      . . . . Order Neuroptera   **lacewing larva**

—   Mouthparts are not long slender tubes 25

25   Animal lives on the surface film and springs high into the air when
      disturbed, using a forked springing organ which is usually folded under
      the end of the abdomen. Most species are tiny (1 mm) but one grows to
      5 mm (Fig. 22) . . . . Order Collembola   **springtail**

—   Animal does not jump like this, and has no springing organ (some
      examples are shown in Fig. 23) . . . . . Order Coleoptera   **beetle larva**

(**Note:** Beetle larvae are a particularly varied group and there are no common characteristics to help recognise
them. If possible check with a reference book illustrating beetle larvae if you reach this point.)

KEY THREE: KEY TO THE ARACHNIDS of British freshwater habitats
Phylum **Arthropoda**, Class **Arachnida**

In addition to the true Arachnids, two other animals are commonly confused with them—and are accordingly included in this key:—

1   Animal with four pairs of true jointed legs (Figs 2–4); may be small or
     large   2

—,   Animal of distinctive shape (Fig. 1). When examined closely it is seen to
     possess clawed, unjointed prolegs. Small (less than 2 mm) and often
     found in damp moss etc   .   .   .   . Phylum TARDIGRADA   **water bear**

2   Animal oval in shape with two suckers under the thorax, which can be
     clearly seen through the body when viewed with a handlens. (It actually
     possesses more than four pairs of legs if examined closely.) (Fig. 2)
              .   . Phylum ARTHROPODA, Class Crustacea, family Argulidae   **fish louse**

—   Animal without suckers; a true Arachnid (Figs 3 and 4)
     .   .   .   . Phylum Arthropoda, Class Arachnida   .   .3

3   Head and body fused into one part, frequently spherical and usually small
     (1–2 mm)—though some still-water mites are much larger (Fig. 3)
     .   .   .   . Order Hydracarina   **water mite**

—   Body formed of two parts with a connecting waist separating the fused
     head-thorax from the abdomen (Fig. 4)   4

4   Animal can swim freely underwater, abdomen covered in short water
     repellent hairs which trap a silver layer of air when it is underwater
     (Fig. 4)
     . Order Araneae, family Agelenidae   ***Argyroneta aquatica* the water spider**

—   Animal unable to swim freely underwater, without water repellent hairs
     over the abdomen; most come from the surface film—but at least one
     genus can run down the bank and catch prey underwater
     .   .   .   . Order Araneae   **terrestrial spider**

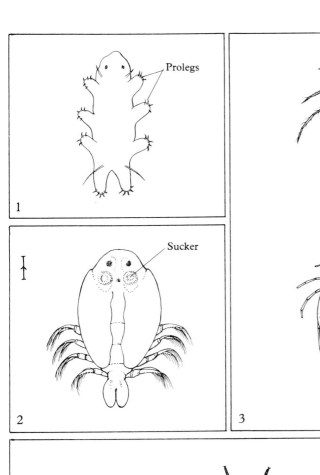

Prolegs

Sucker

1

2

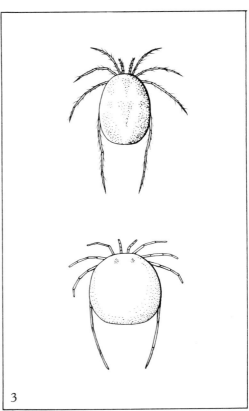

3

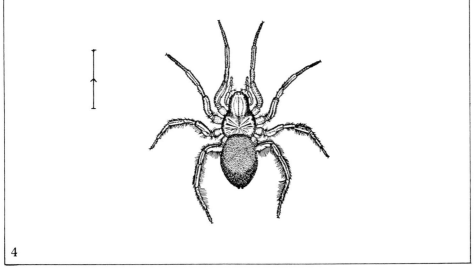

4

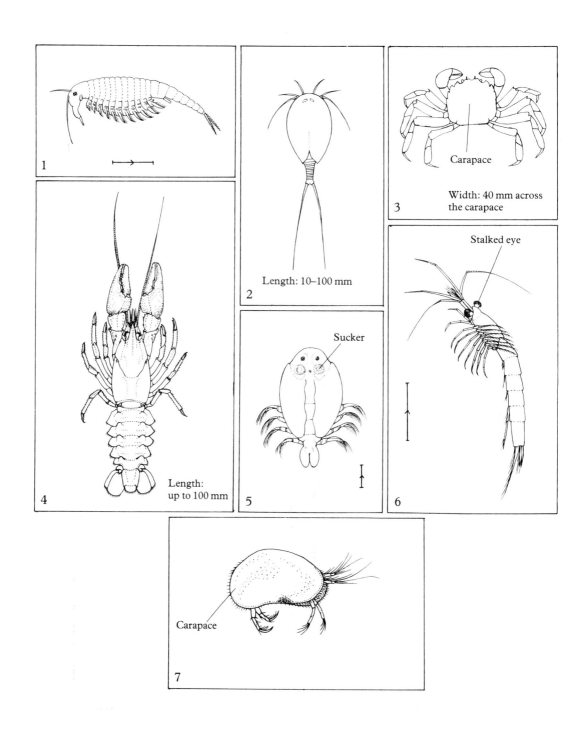

1

2

Length: 10–100 mm

3

Carapace

Width: 40 mm across
the carapace

4

Length:
up to 100 mm

5

Sucker

6

Stalked eye

7

Carapace

KEY FOUR: KEY TO THE FRESHWATER CRUSTACEA
(Phylum **Arthropoda,** Class   **Crustacea**)

Two, rarely found, crustacean species of distinctive appearance are not included in the key. They are both found in temporary pools: Order Anostracea, family Chirocephalidae *Chirocephalus diaphanus,* **the fairy shrimp** (Fig. 1) and Order Notostraca, family Triopsidae *Triops cancriformis* (Fig. 2).

1   Animal with an obvious carapace—a fusion of the dorsal skeletal plates to form a protective cover over at least the thorax, and sometimes the whole body (Figs 3–9) 2

—   Animal without an obvious carapace 9

2   Animal equipped with a pair of pincers or chelae (Figs 3 and 4) 3

—   Animal without pincers (Figs 5–9).   4

3   Animal a crab, no abdominal segments visible from above (Fig. 3)
    .   .Order Decapoda, family Grapsidae,   *Eriocheir sinensis* **the mitten crab**

—   Animal resembling a small lobster; abdomen and "tail" visible from above (Fig. 4)   .   .   . Order Decapoda, family Astacidae   **freshwater crayfish**

4   Animal oval in shape with two suckers on the underside of the thorax which can clearly be seen, through the body, using a handlens (Fig. 5)
    .   .   .   . Order Branchiura, family Argulidae   **fish louse**

—   Animal without suckers (Fig. 6 on)   5

5   Eyes on stalks, resembling a marine shrimp or prawn (Fig 6)
    .   .   .   . Order Mysidacea, family Mysidae   **opossum shrimp**

—   Eyes not stalked, no close resemblance to a true shrimp.   6

6   Animal totally enclosed in a kidney-shaped carapace, from which legs protrude when swimming; this activity resembles the bumbling of a distraught runner bean seed. Frequently becomes trapped in the surface film when captured. Rarely more than 2 mm long (Fig. 7)
    .   .   .   . Order Ostracoda   **ostracod**

—   Carapace never enclosing the whole animal in this way. Animals from the plankton community (although may rest amongst water weeds by day) and most, but not all, less than 2 mm long. Swim with jerky movements 7

7   Carapace enclosing all but the head and antennae, which are enlarged to
     form swimming organs (Fig. 8) . . . . Order Cladocera   **water flea**

—   Carapace does not enclose the abdomen. Animal may (or may not) have
     antennae enlarged to form swimming organs 8

8   Animal pear-shaped, with a single eye (usually red) in the centre of the
     head. Antennae not forming swimming organs, legs are used for this
     purpose. Females often bearing two egg masses at the rear end (Fig. 9)
     . . . . Order Copepoda, loosely called "Cyclops" or   **water flea**

—   Antennae forming swimming organs, two eyes; eggs, if present, not in two
     masses at the rear end. Rare planktonic predators (Fig. 10)
     . . . . Order Cladocera   **predatory water flea**

9   Animal less than 2 mm long 10

—   Animal more than 2 mm long 11

10   **Look carefully and closely at your specimen to ensure that you
     were correct in couplet 1.**
     Animal with a carapace (compare with Figs 7–9) 7

—   Animal without a carapace 11

11   Animal flattened from side-to-side, active swimmers when disturbed
     (Figs 11 and 12) 12

—   Animal flattened from top-to-bottom; resembles a woodlouse (to which it
     is related) (Fig. 13) . . Order Isopoda, family Asellidae   **freshwater hog louse**

12   Second antennae uniquely characteristic—very robust, more than half as
     long as the body and used in walking and burrowing; found in lowland
     rivers (Fig. 11) . . . . Order Amphipoda, family Corophiidae   ***Corophium***

—   Second antennae not more than half as long as the body which is curved at
     rest. Often found paired (male and female); very common invertebrate of
     streams and pools of all sizes (Fig. 12)
     . . . . Order Amphipoda, family Gammaridae   **freshwater shrimp**

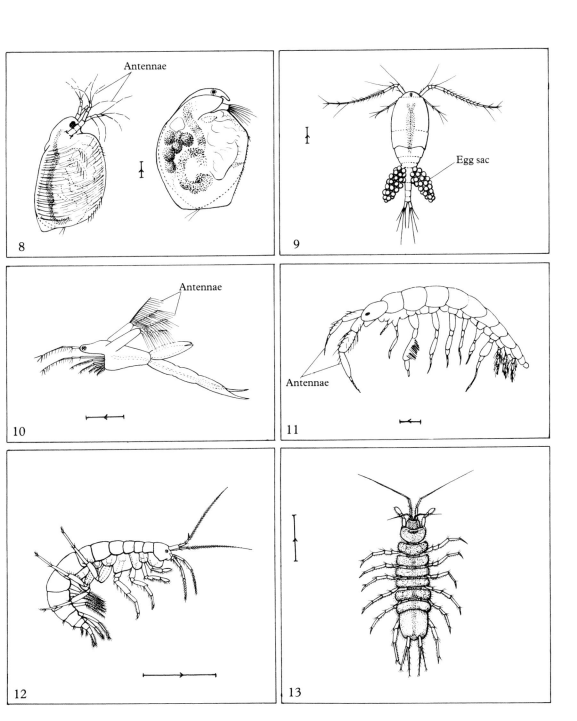

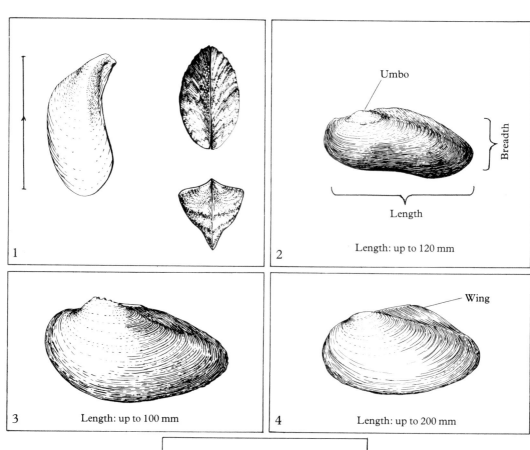

Umbo

Breadth

Length

Length: up to 120 mm

Length: up to 100 mm

Wing

Length: up to 200 mm

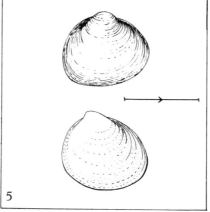

KEY FIVE: KEY TO THE FRESHWATER BIVALVES
(Phylum **Mollusca,** Class **Bivalvia**)

Note: the umbo is the point of origin of growth of the shell and is therefore surrounded by the rings of growth showing on the shell pattern.

1   In life the shell is attached to stones and logs by secreted threads (the byssus—like that of the marine edible mussel); it is unlikely to be collected without this being apparent. The shell is almost triangular in section, and acquires its common name from the black and white/yellow striping (which may be obscured by dark green algal growth in productive waters) (Fig. 1)

. . . . Order Cyrenodonta, family Dreissenidae ***Dreissena polymorpha*** **zebra mussel**

—   Shell never attached; rounded in section, not angular 2

2   Shell valve at least 1.5 times as long as broad. Adult specimens large— more than 30 mm long (Figs 2–4) 3

—   Shell valve not much longer than broad, and never as much as 1.5 times as long; adult shell smaller, most species under 15 mm, the largest always under 30 mm (Fig. 5)

. . . . Order Cyrenodonta, family Sphaeriidae **orb cockle** or **pea mussel**

3   Definite depression both between the umbo and the "blunt" end of the shell, and between the two umbos when viewed from above the hinge (Figs 2 and 3) 4

—   No definite depressions between the umbo and the "blunt" end, or between the two umbos—which therefore meet along the line of the hinge. Shell often with a wing which may be pronounced (Fig. 4)

. . . Order Unionoida, family Unionidae ***Anadonta*** **swan** or **duck mussel**

4   Shell with a concave lower margin (i.e. the side opposite the umbo is curved inwards towards the main body) making it almost kidney-shaped. Shell colour black. From fast-flowing rivers, and lakes through which such rivers run (Fig. 2)

. . .Order Unionoida, family Margaritiferidae ***Margaritifer margaritifer*** **pearl mussel**

—   Shell with a convex lower margin (i.e., the side opposite the umbo is curved outwards away from the main body). Colour black, green or yellow (Fig. 3) . . . . Order Unionoida, family Unionidae ***Unio***

KEY SIX: KEY TO THE FRESHWATER SNAILS
(Phylum **Mollusca**, Class **Gastropoda**)

Note: Terrestrial species which feed on emergent vegetation are not included—examine the vegetation before sampling. For explanation of the terms tall and broad see Fig. 1; for sinistral and dextral see Figs 8 and 9. Only animals collected alive can be identified using this key, the operculum is not retained for long after death.

1   Shell with a plate or door (an operculum) which can seal off the aperture to the shell when the animal is made to retract. Prod through the shell opening—the operculum feels hard or horny (Fig. 1) 2

—   Shell without an operculum: prod it—it feels squishy 5

2   Shell as broad as, or broader than, tall (Figs 2 and 3) 3

—   Shell taller than broad (Figs 4 and 5) 4

3   Spire very short; the last whorl dominates the overall shape of the shell, shell often dark with pale spots, operculum with bright orange or red fringe (Fig. 2)
                  Order Prosobranchia, family Neritidae   ***Theodoxus fluviatilis*** **nerite**

—   Shell may be a spiral or a coil, but the whorls gradually enlarge from the growing point to the aperture; no bright fringe to the operculum (Fig. 3)
  . . . . Order Prosobranchia, family Hydrobiidae,
                 family Valvatidae   ***Valvata*** **valve snail**

4   Shell banded, and often large (up to 40 mm). If the shell is dark green in colour rub it to remove algae (Fig. 4)
    . . . . Order Prosobranchia, family Viviparidae   ***Viviparus*** **banded snail**

—   Shell never banded, though may be pale or blotched. Many species are small (1–3 mm) though the largest can reach 15 mm (Fig. 5)
    . . . . Order Prosobranchia, family Hydrobiidae **spire shell**

5   Shell neither a coil nor a spiral—characteristically "limpet" shaped (Fig. 6) . . . . . . Order Pulmonata, family Ancylidae **freshwater limpet**

—   Shell either a coil or a spiral (Figs 7–9) 6

6   Shell coiled (as in a Catherine wheel) (Fig. 7)
    . . . . Order Pulmonata, family Planorbiidae **ramshorn snail**

—   Shell a spiral (Figs 8 and 9) 7

7   Shell sinistral, or left-handed⋆, relatively fragile (Fig. 8)
    . . . . Order Pulmonata, family Physidae **bladder snail**

—   Shell dextral, or right handed⋆, may be fragile or robust (Fig. 9)
    . . . . Order Pulmonata, family Lymnaeidae **pond snail**

⋆Sinistral and dextral spiralling can be reversed in some individuals, usually only a tiny proportion of the population. Some species of pond snails (usually those with robust shells) have a higher proportion of sinistral individuals within certain populations than is usual. In most sites this character can be used with safety.

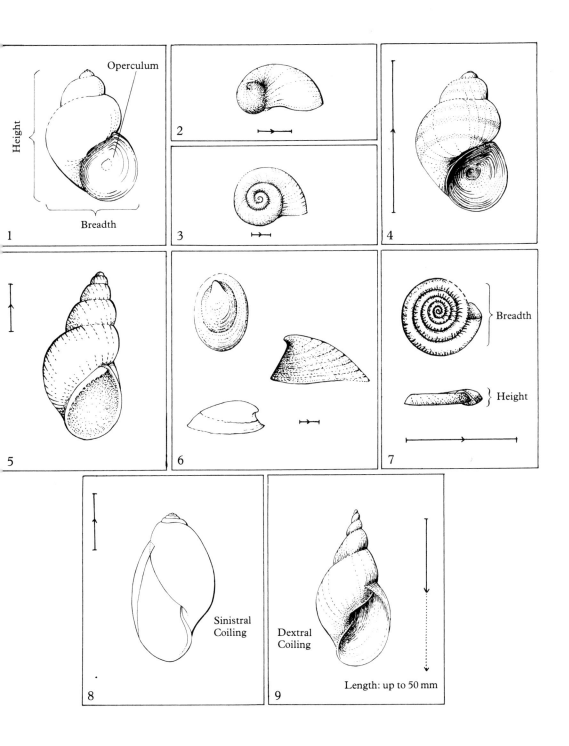

Operculum

Height

Breadth

1

2

3

4

5

6

Breadth

Height

7

Sinistral
Coiling

8

Dextral
Coiling

Length: up to 50 mm

9

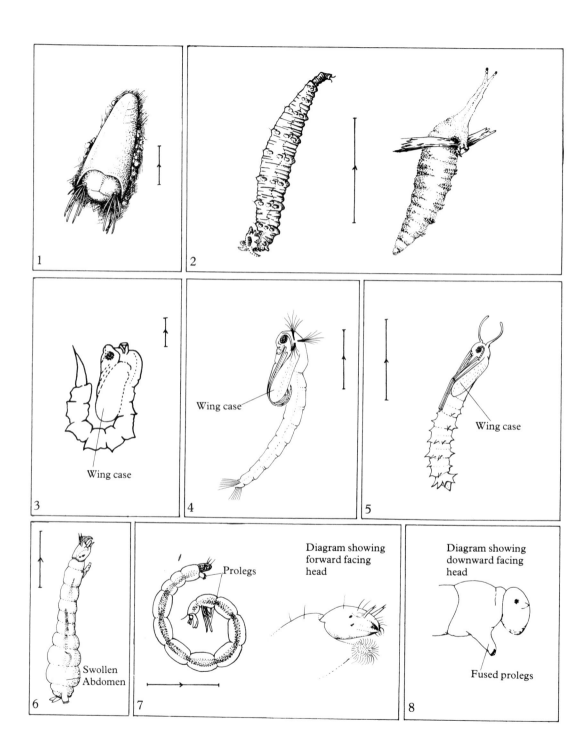

KEY SEVEN: KEY TO THE FAMILIES OF TRUE FLIES
based on characters shown by their aquatic larvae and pupae
(Phylum **Arthropoda,** Class **Insecta,** Order **Diptera**)

Note: Diptera is a very large order, and one of the least well-known taxonomically; this key identifies the most commonly found of the easily recognisable families but leaves the remainder as "other Diptera".

1 Animal in a straw coloured/brown puparium (a case in which pupation can occur) shaped like a cream-horn (Fig. 1) and attached to a stone or a plant in a stream. . . . . .family Simuliidae **blackfly pupa**

— Animal not in a puparium like this. 2

2 Animal a brown/red, inactive, chrysalis stage; the maggot's skin has hardened and changed colour when pupation occurred (Fig 2) . . . . inactive pupa of a family in the Sub-Order Cyclorrhapha

— Animal not in a hardened brown/red chrysalis form. It is either an active pupa or a larva 3

3 Animal with obvious swollen wing cases on the thorax (Figs 3–5) 4

— Animal without swollen wing cases on the thorax. 6

4 Animal bent into a definite U-shape at rest (Fig. 3) . . . . family Dixidae **meniscus midge pupa**

— Animal straight or slightly curved at rest, only flexes into a U-shape when swimming. 5

5 Thorax very swollen making the animal look "hunch-backed" when seen from the side: thorax wider than, or as wide as, the head (Fig. 4) . . . . family Chironomidae **non-biting midge pupa**

— Pupa never with thorax so swollen as to be as wide as the head when seen from the side (e.g. Fig. 5). . . . .pupa from one of many other Dipteran families

6 Animal attached by its rear end to the substrate, moving by looping; produces silk threads during this process which may "trap" other animals in the sample. Posterior part of the abdomen noticeably swollen. Always from running water (Fig. 6). . . . . .family Simuliidae **blackfly larva**

— Never attached to substrate or moving by looping. Rear of abdomen not swollen. 7

7 Animal with a head capsule, this is straw coloured/brown and is equipped with eyes, antennae and mouthparts (use a lens) (Figs 7–11) 8

— Animal without a head capsule but a pair of jaws can be seen inside the head of the maggot (use a lens). *Beware* of species with false eyes at the rear end—the head is at the front when the animal moves! (Fig. 16). 14

8 Animal swims using a characteristic figure-of-eight wriggling motion. It possesses two pairs of prolegs, one on the first thoracic segment and one on the last abdominal segment. Care should be taken to look for these with a lens if the animal is not swimming—they are not very obvious in some species (Fig. 7) 9

— Animal may wriggle, but not using a figure-of-eight motion. It may, or may not, have prolegs—but there are never two pairs distributed as above . . 10

9 Animal from moss or other vegetation found in stony streams or springheads; the head characteristically points downwards, and the front pair of prolegs is fused into one organ (Fig 8) . . . . family Thaumaleidae

—   Animal from any freshwater habitat; head held horizontally, front prolegs
      separate. Some common species are blood red, others, equally common,
      are not (Fig. 7)
      . . . . family Chironomidae **non–biting midge larvae**
                                    (red ones are called "bloodworms")

10   Larva transparent with two pairs of black air sacs, one pair at the front,
      the other near the back. Found in midwater, swims by quick flicks of the
      body
      (Fig. 9). . . . . family Chaoboridae   **"ghost" larva**

—   May or may not be transparent, but if so then without black air sacs 11

11   Head, and also body segments, twice as long as broad. Swims with a
      sinuous snake-like motion (Fig. 10)
      . . . . .family Ceratopogonidae   **biting midge larva**

—   Head never twice as long as broad, does not swim like a snake 12

12   Animal with swollen thorax. Suspended from the surface film in life,
      either hanging down at a steep angle to it, or lying parallel with it (Fig. 11)
      . . . . family Culicidae   **mosquito larva**

—   Thorax not swollen, animal not hanging from the surface film of open
      water 13

13   Animal resting in the meniscus at the side of the dish, stone, etc. forming
      an inverted U-shape (n-shape) when at rest. Has distinctive "posterior
      paddles" at the rear of its abdomen (Fig. 12)
      . . . . family Dixidae   **meniscus midge larva**

—   Animal not resting in an inverted U-shape; without posterior paddles
      . . . . larva from one of the many other families of Diptera

14   Animal with a single "tail" which is at least half as long as its body, and
      often longer than the body (Figs 13 and 14). 15

—   Animal without a "tail", or with a very short one 16

15   Obvious thickenings between the body segments, larva without prolegs,
      and with a "tail" which rarely equals the body length (Fig. 13)
      . . . . family Ptychopteridae

—   Larva possesses several pairs of obvious prolegs, but lacks thickenings
      between the body segments; in some species the "tail" can be up to four
      times the body length when fully extended (Fig 14)
      . . . . family Syrphidae   **rat-tailed maggot**

16   Animal possessing either a six-lobed plate at the rear end in which can be
      seen two black dots (spiracles) OR with two to six short tails but devoid
      of spines or thickenings on or between the abdominal segments (Fig. 15)
      . . . . family Tipulidae **crane fly larvae** and their relatives

—   Animal without a six lobed plate of this kind. If it has tails, then it also
      possesses spines and/or distinct thickenings on the abdominal segments
      (Fig. 16) . . . . larva from one of the many other families of Diptera

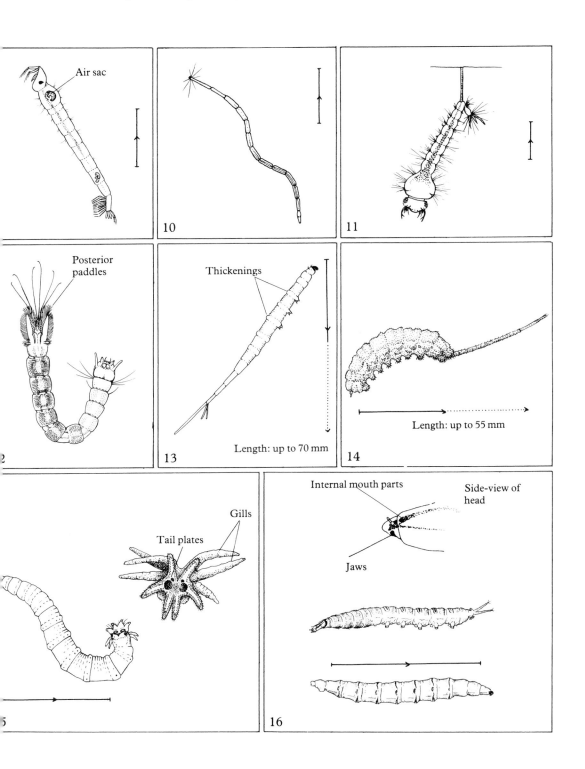

Air sac

10

11

Posterior
paddles

Thickenings

Length: up to 55 mm

Length: up to 70 mm

13

14

Gills

Tail plates

Internal mouth parts

Side-view of
head

Jaws

16

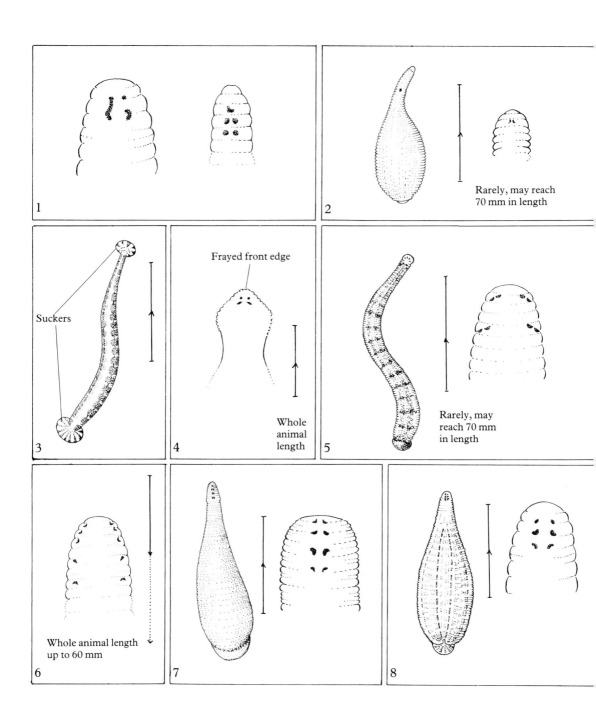

KEY EIGHT: KEY TO THE FAMILIES OF LEECHES
(Phylum **Annelida,** Class **Hirudinea**)

1   Leech with one to five pairs of eyespots (all figs) 2

—   Leech apparently without eyespots. All leeches actually have eyespots, but sometimes they are difficult to find. Look hard, but if you really can't find any, move to 7

2   Leech with one or two pairs of eyespots (Figs 2–4) 3

—   Leech with three to five pairs of eyespots (Figs 5–8) 7

3   Eyespots have fused together to form irregular patches of pigment. Fusions can be of all the eyes, or just two (Fig. 1)
. . . . Order Rhynchobdellae, family Glossiphonidae

—   No fusions; each eyespot is symmetrical and is a mirror-image of the other member of the pair 4

4   Leech with one pair of eyespots (Fig. 2)
. . . . Order Rhynchobdellae, family Glossiphonidae

—   Leech with two pairs of eyespots (Figs 3 and 4) 5

5   Eyespots arranged as the front two pairs of Fig. 5. If you look at the animal again you will find the other two pairs of eyespots further back on the head . . . . Order Pharyngobdellae, family Erpobdellidae

—   Eyespots not arranged as in Fig. 5, pairs more nearly one behind the other . . 6

6   Both suckers very distinct, body long and thin (Fig. 3)
. . . . Order Rhynchobdellae, family Piscicolidae

—   Front sucker not distinctly rounded though there is a slight "neck". Front of the head with a rather "frayed" appearance (Fig. 4)
. . . . Order Rhynchobdellae, family Glossiphonidae

7   Leech with five pairs of eyespots which can sometimes be very difficult to see in living specimens as the background colour is dark. When mature, and resting, animal is very long (40–50 mm) and fat (10–12 mm) (Fig. 6)
. . . . Order Gnathobdellae, family Hirudinidae

—   Leech with three or four pairs of eyespots. One family has a very dark background colour against which the eyes are difficult, but never imposs-ible, to see: the mature animal can reach 4 cm long but is not as fat as the Hirudinidae (8 mm or less) 8

8   Four pairs of eyes arranged in two horizontal rows (Fig. 5)
. . . . Order Pharyngobdellae, family Erpobdellidae

—   Three or four pairs of eyes arranged in longitudinal lines down the centre of the head (Figs 7 and 8). . . . . Order Rhynchobdellae, family Glossiphonidae

KEY NINE: KEY TO THE FAMILIES OF WATER BUGS
(Phylum **Arthropoda,** Class **Insecta,** Order **Hemiptera**)

1   Antennae conspicuous, at least as long as the head: animal living on top of
    the surface film; (Figs 1–3) 2
—   Antennae inconspicuous, cannot be seen from above. Animal living under
    water; it may, or may not, cling to the underside of the surface film (make
    sure to give it deep enough water!) (Figs 4–9) 5

2   Head over four times as long as broad, whole animal long and thin (Fig. 1)
    . . . . family Hydrometridae **water measurer**
—   Head about as broad as long, whole animal not extremely thin (Figs 2
    and 3) 3

3   Second pair of legs 1.5 times the length of head and body combined; when
    legs are spread (in life) outline is broader than long (Fig. 2)
    . . . . family Gerridae **pond skater**
—   Second pair of legs never 1.5 times longer than head and body length;
    when legs are spread (in life) outline is at least as long as broad 4

4   Animal over 4 mm long, with an orange stripe down the side (Fig. 3)
    . . . . family Veliidae **water cricket**
—   Animal less than 4 mm long, without an orange stripe. A group of families
    which are difficult to separate
    . . . . families Veliidae, Mesoveliidae, Hebridae, Saldidae

5   Animal with a single tail (long in adults, short in nymphs) (Fig. 4)
    . . . . family Nepidae **water scorpion** or **stick insect**
—   Animal without a tail 6

6   Animal swims "upside down" (legs at the top, "back" at the bottom) as
    air is stored in two channels fringed with hairs on what would normally be
    the underside of the abdomen (Figs 5 and 6) 7
—   Animal swims usual side up; there are no channels fringed with hairs on
    the underside of the abdomen (Fig. 7 onwards) 8

7   Hind limbs about twice as long as the other two pairs, adults (with wings)
    at least 1 cm long (Fig. 5). . . family Notonectidae **greater water boatman**
—   Hind limbs about the same size as the other two pairs, adults 2–3 mm
    (Fig. 6). . . . . family Pleidae

8   Swims by rowing with an elongated, hair-fringed, third pair of limbs;
    mouthparts are a triangular flap, not a piercing "beak" (Fig. 7)
    . . . . family Corixidae **lesser water boatman**
—   The hind pair of limbs are not the only ones used for swimming; mouth-
    parts modified to a piercing "beak" (which may be very long and be
    folded under the abdomen) (Figs 8 and 9) 9

9   Front pair of limbs strongly modified for grasping, eyes bright red, head
    sunk into thorax making a rounded outline to the body. From still waters
    (Fig. 8). . . . . family Naucoridae **saucer bug**
—   Front legs not modified for grasping, head protrudes from outline, wings
    usually reduced in adult. From fast-flowing rivers (Fig. 9)
    . . . . family Aphelocheiridae

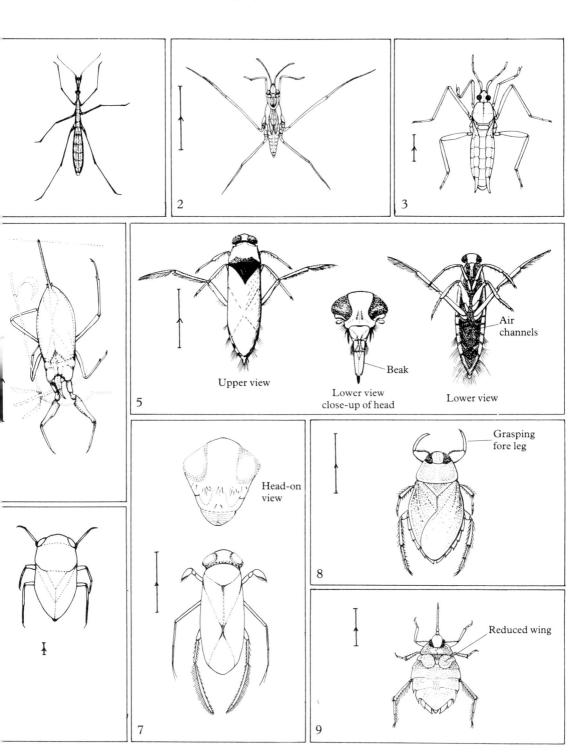

Upper view

Lower view
close-up of head

Beak

Lower view

Air
channels

Head-on
view

Grasping
fore leg

Reduced wing

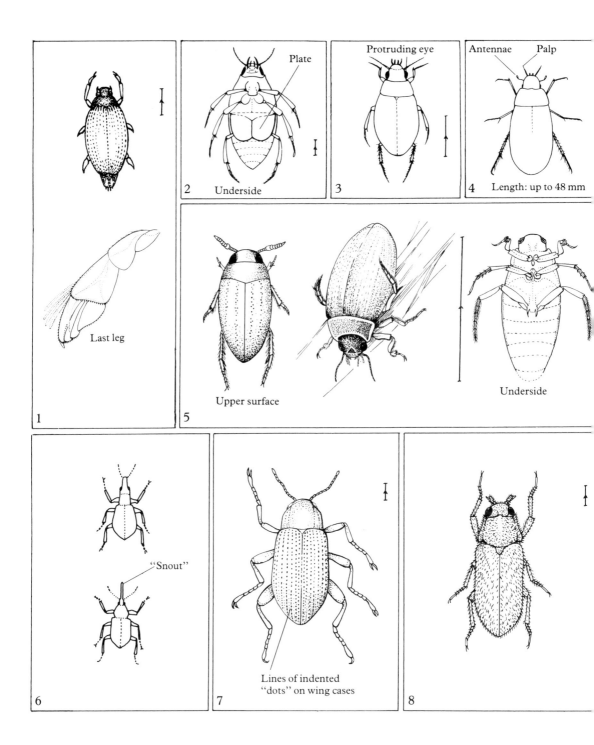

1

Last leg

2 Underside

Plate

3 Protruding eye

4 Antennae Palp

Length: up to 48 mm

5 Upper surface

Underside

6 "Snout"

7 Lines of indented "dots" on wing cases

8

KEY TEN: KEY TO THE FAMILIES OF WATER BEETLES (Adults only)
(Phylum **Arthropoda,** Class **Insecta,** Order **Coleoptera**)

1   Animal rests on the surface film, dashes around in circles and dives frequently. If it stays still you will see that the second and third pair of legs are modified to form short paddle-blades (Fig. 1)
. . . . family Gyrinidae **whirligig beetle**

—   Animal visits underside of surface film, but does not dash around in circles on it. Legs often modified for swimming, but never in the form of short paddle-blades (Figs 2 onwards). 2

2   Strong swimmers whose hind legs, at least, are equipped with a fringe of hairs to aid this activity (Figs 2–5). 3

—   Non-swimmers, no such fringe of hairs on the hind legs (Figs 6–8) 6

3   The bases of the hind limbs are obscured by large plates, these are most easily seen by putting the animal in a transparent dish and looking from underneath (Fig. 2). . . . . family Haliplidae

—   Bases of the hind limbs not covered by large plates (Figs 3–5) 4

4   Animal usually makes loud squeaking noises when caught. The head protrudes from the thorax, and the eyes protrude from the head (Fig. 3)
. . . . family Hygrobiidae **screech beetle**

—   Animal cannot squeak. The head fits smoothly into the thorax making a well-rounded silhouette. The eyes do not protrude (Figs 4 and 5) 5

5   The underside of the body covered with short hairs which hold a glistening bubble when submerged . The palps (part of the mouthparts) are very well developed and often as long as, or even longer than, the antennae (palps have only 3–4 segments, antennae 7–10) (Fig. 4) . . family Hydrophilidae

—   The underside of the body is not covered with short hairs, so no silver bubble can be seen when submerged. The palps are much shorter than the antennae (Fig. 5) . . . . family Dytiscidae **diving beetle**

6   Head protrudes into a conspicuous snout (Fig. 6)
. . . . family Curculionidae **weevil**

—   Head not protruding into a snout (Figs 7 and 8) 7

7   Animal with dots ("punctures") arranged in lines down the wing covers, which are without obvious downy hairs; strong claws for gripping the stones in the streams and upland lakes in which it lives. Antennae filamentous throughout (Fig. 7) . . . . . family Elminthidae **riffle beetle**

—   Animal with downy hair on the wing covers, "punctures" are not arranged in regular lines; claws less well developed. Antennae with a distinct swelling near the base (Fig. 8) . . . . .family Dryopidae

KEY ELEVEN: KEY TO THE FAMILIES OF MAYFLIES (Nymphs)
(Phylum **Arthropoda,** Class **Insecta,** Order **Ephemeroptera**)

Note: The gills are an important feature of mayfly identification; look at them carefully with a lens. Some are plates, looking like transparent leaves with the trachea arranged like leaf-veins; others are tufts of filaments which never resemble leaf veins; some combine both features—look carefully! Remember tails taper to a point if unbroken, if left and right tails are unequal or if any has a sudden ending—they have been broken on capture.

1   Gills held over, or attached to, the top of the abdomen; they barely protrude beyond the body outline (in some groups one pair of gills, either the first or the last, will be on the sides, but these are very reduced in size compared with the others) (Figs 1–3). 2

—   All pairs of gills attached to, and pointing away from, the sides of the abdomen (Figs 4 onwards) 4

2   One pair of gills modified to form covers for all but the first pair; the other pairs can be seen waving under the covers in life. Body often hairy and covered in silt (Fig. 1). . . . . family Caenidae

—   No gill covers 3

3   Legs and tails striped yellow/white like a zebra crossing. Gills are continuously fluttered in life and are leaf-like. The body is dark in colour (Fig. 2). . . . . family Ephemerellidae

—   Gills large and feathery and continuously waved over the back in life. Body is yellow, legs are not striped (Fig. 3)
. . . . family Ephemeridae **burrowing mayfly nymph**

4   Animal obviously flattened from top-to-bottom, often walks sideways rapidly like a crab. Head almost a half-moon shape. Front legs with a broad femur which sticks out at right angles to the thorax. Gills a plate with a basal tuft of filaments (though the filaments are difficult to see) (Fig. 4). . . . . family Ecdyonuridae **flattened mayfly nymph**

—   Nymph never strongly flattened, cylindrical in form with a "pointed" head (Figs 5 onwards). 5

5   Gills either a tuft of feathery filaments OR a forked or many branched filament with a remnant plate at the base. Swimming laboured and never darting. Tails of some, but not all, species can be as long as the body (Fig. 5). 6

—   Gills a plate, care must be taken to look for the outline, as it is transparent, and not to mistake the leaf-like pattern of the trachea for a tuft of filaments. Animal a strong swimmer, darting swiftly through the water (Fig. 6). 7

6   Gills feathery consisting of two branches thickly fringed with filaments (as in the family Ephemeridae, Fig. 3); one species only, which has rarely been recorded from Britain . . . . family Potamanthidae

—   Gills a forked or many branched filament, but always with a remnant plate at least at the base. Tails long (Fig. 5) . . . . .family Leptophlebiidae

7   The middle tail shorter than the outer two—beware of broken tails! (Fig. 6). . . . . family Baetidae **swimming mayfly nymph**

—   All three tails the same length 8

8   Distinct black rings on the tails (not just segment junctions); there may, or may not, also be a black band near the tip of the tails (Fig. 6)
. . . . family Baetidae **swimming mayfly nymph**

—   Tails always with a black band near the tip but **never** with black rings between this band and the base of the tails (there are segment junctions but these do not appear dark black) (Fig. 7). . . . . . family Siphlonuridae

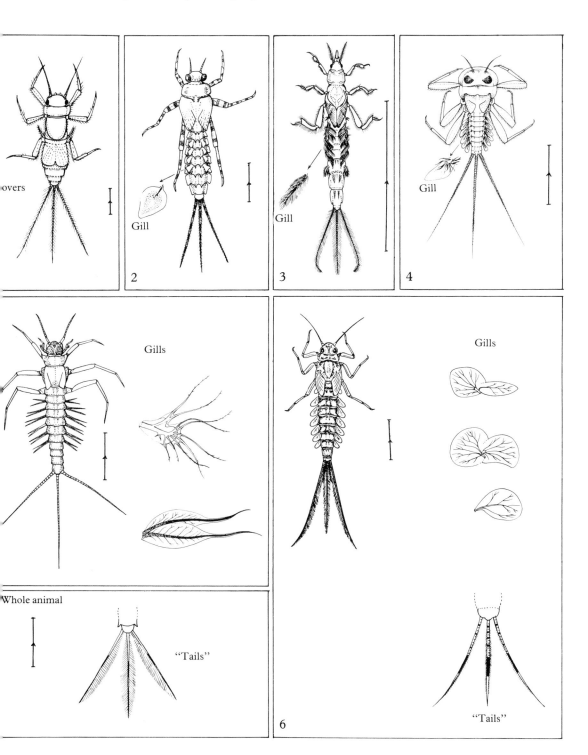

overs

2

Gill

3

Gill

4

Gill

Gills

Whole animal

"Tails"

6

Gills

"Tails"

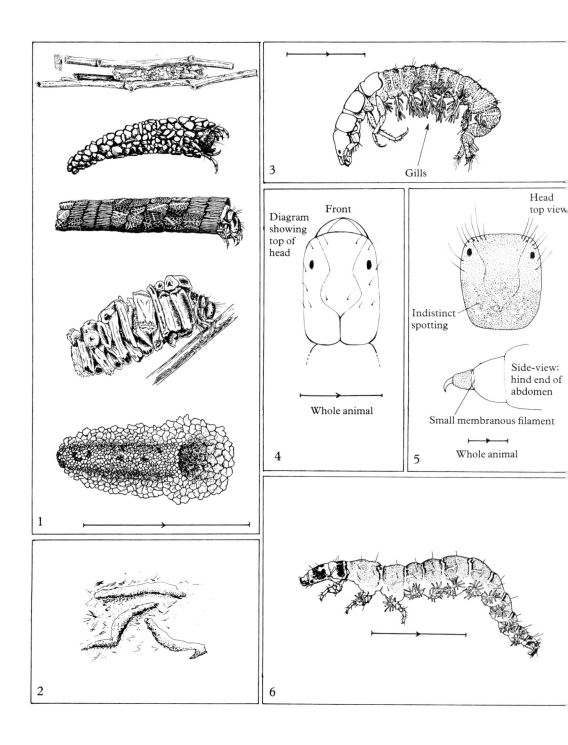

3

Gills

4

Diagram showing top of head

Front

Whole animal

5

Head top view

Indistinct spotting

Side-view: hind end of abdomen

Small membranous filament

Whole animal

1

2

6

KEY TWELVE: KEY TO THE FAMILIES OF CADDIS FLIES (larvae)
(Phylum **Arthropoda**, Class **Insecta**, Order **Trichoptera**)

Note: The object of this key is to separate out as many families as possible using characteristics that can be seen without removing the animal from its case (if it has one). The animal can then be returned to the water unharmed. Characters have not been found to separate all families in this way: a note to this effect is included where relevant. Regrettably the Limnephilidae, the largest family, is among these. The key works best for larvae collected from running water.

1   Animal living in a case that it drags around with it, or in a long silk tube, usually covered in silt particles attached to a stone (Figs 1 and 2) 2

—   Animal free-living, not in a case or tube 6

2   Animal living in a "mobile case" (Fig. 1) 11

—   Animal living in a long silk tube (Fig. 2). 3

3   Tufted gills present underneath the abdomen (Fig. 3). Larva living in a wind-sock shaped net with which it traps its food (the net may have been destroyed when the specimen was collected) . . . . . family Hydropsychidae

—   Animal without abdominal gills 4

4   Animal with a distinctive elongated oval head which is 1.5 times as long as broad (Fig. 4). The combination of an orange/light brown head and a yellow/white body is also distinctive in some, but not all, species. Living in a wind-sock shaped net in which it traps its food . . . family Philopotamidae

—   Head not much longer than broad, and never exceeding 1.25 times as long. Never combining an orange head with a white/yellow body (Figs 5 and 7) 5

5   Hooks attached to the hind end of the abdomen by a membranous filament which is as long as the hardened shaft of the hook; head usually conspicuously spotted, body often pink (Fig. 7). Living in a wind-sock shaped net in which it traps its food . . . . family Polycentropidae

—   Hooks without obvious membranous filament attaching them to the body. Head may be indistinctly spotted. Living in an elongated silk tube attached to a rock (which may be damaged on collection) (Figs 2 and 5) . . . . family Psychomyiidae

6   Animal with tufts of gills, either underneath (ventral) or at the sides (lateral) of the abdomen (Figs 3 and 6) 7

—   Animal without abdominal gills 8

7   Abdominal gills ventral, animal often rolls into a ball, and swims with an exaggerated side-to-side movement of the back end. Colour grey or brown (Fig. 3). family Hydropsychidae

—   Abdominal gills lateral, animal swims with an up and down movement of the abdomen. Colour often green or green/brown (Fig. 6) . . . . family Rhyacophilidae

8   Hooks at the end of the abdomen are relatively large, "mounted" facing to the rear (usually) on flexible basal filaments—they can be used as grappling hooks for backward movement. No case-supporting structures on the first abdominal segment (Figs 5 and 7) 9

—   Hooks relatively small, "mounted" facing outwards on a rigid base to support the case (which has been lost in sampling). Fleshy protruberances (case-bearing structures) often present either on the dorsal surface and/or the sides of the first abdominal segment (Fig. 8)
. . . . larva of a cased caddis which has lost its case

9   Animal with a distinctive elongated oval head which is 1.5 times as long as broad (Fig. 4). The combination of an orange/light brown head and a yellow/white body is also distinctive in some, but not all, species. Living in a wind-sock shaped net in which it traps its food (which may be destroyed in sampling . . . . family Philopotamidae

—   Head not much longer than broad, and never exceeding 1.25 times as long. Never combining an orange head with a white/yellow body (Figs 5 and 7) 10

10   Hooks attached to the abdomen by a membranous filament which is as long as the hardened shaft of the hook; head usually conspicuously spotted, body often pink (Fig. 7). Living in a wind-sock shaped net in which it traps its food, but this may be destroyed by sampling
. . . . family Polycentropidae

—   Hooks without obvious membranous filament attaching them to the body. Head may be indistinctly spotted. Living in an elongated silk tube attached to a rock (which may be damaged on collection) (Figs 2 and 5)
. . . . family Psychomyiidae

11   Case neatly and symmetrically constructed from sand, small stones or fragments of vegetation 12

—   Case built without regard for neatness or symmetry, may incorporate many different types of material (e.g. Fig. 9).
Many families key out here
—a good character has not been found to differentiate between them

12   Case constructed from plant fragments 13

—   Case constructed from pure silk, sand or gravel 16

13   Plant fragments arranged in a spiral pattern (Figs 10 and 11) 14

—   Plant fragments not arranged in such a spiral 15

14   Case small (2 cm), tapers to a point: animal with a long third pair of limbs with which it swims—case and all (Fig. 10) . . . . family Leptoceridae

—   Case, when the larva approaches full size, is large (up to 6 cm)—more nearly cylindrical than tapering and open at both ends (as the larva grows it adds more material to the front end but removes the back). Cannot swim but frequently abandons the case when captured. Predator, with grasping forelimbs (Fig. 11) . . . . family Phryganeidae

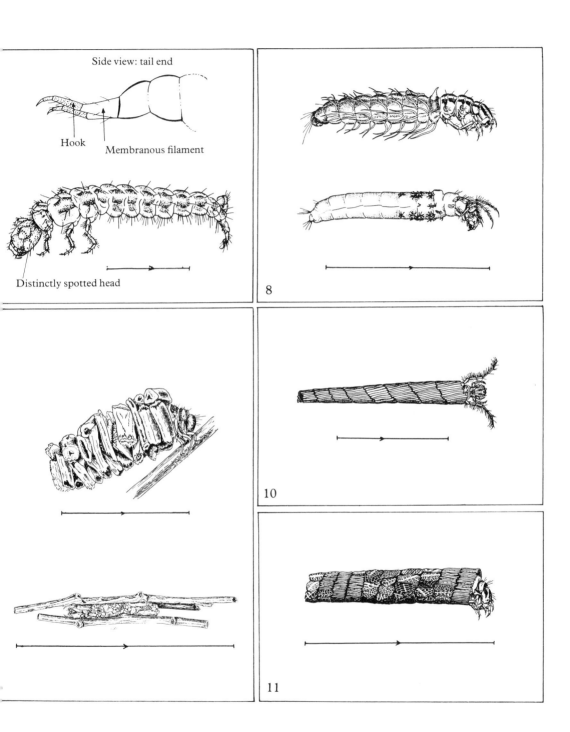

Side view: tail end

Hook

Membranous filament

Distinctly spotted head

8

10

11

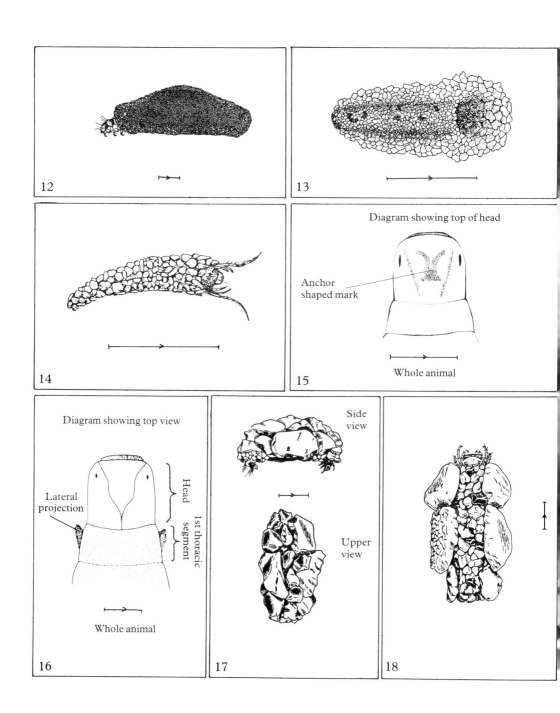

12

13

14

15
Diagram showing top of head

Anchor
shaped mark

Whole animal

16
Diagram showing top view

Lateral
projection

Head

1st thoracic segment

Whole animal

17
Side
view

Upper
view

18

15 Case minute (1 cm or less), drop-shaped and covered with algae, often
    almost transparent (Fig. 12) . . . .   family Hydroptilidae

—   Case not drop-shaped, made of larger vegetation fragments . . . . .
    many families key out here—a good character has not been found to
                                                    differentiate between them

16 Case minute (1 cm or less) and drop shaped. May be transparent silk, or
    covered with silt or fine sand (Fig 12). . . . .   family Hydroptilidae

—   Case not drop-shaped, made of sand or gravel 17

17 Case a tube of sand grains with large lateral extensions ("wings") which
    double its width; usually on the sandy shores of lakes (Fig. 13)
    . . . .   family Molannidae

—   Case without large lateral extensions 18

18 Case a curved cylinder of sand grains (Fig. 14) 19
—   Case not such a curved cylinder of sand grains (Figs 17 and 18) 22

19 Third pair of legs three times as long as the first pair and poke out of the
    case in a characteristic crescent (Fig. 14). 20

—   Third pair of legs never more than twice as long as the first pair and do not
    form the same crescent   21

20 *For this separation the animal must be removed from its case, or a little of the
    front of the case cut away, you may prefer to leave the identification at this
    stage.*

—   Lateral side of first thoracic segment bearing forward pointing projection;
    relatively rare (Fig. 16) . . . .   family Beraeidae

—   No such projection; common . . . .   family Leptoceridae

21 Distinctive anchor-shaped mark on the head, which can be seen by
    looking into the mouth of the case using a lens (Fig. 15)   .   family Odontoceridae

—   No such anchor-shaped mark . . . .
    Many families key out here
    . . . . .   —a good character has not been found to differentiate between them

22 Case flat-bottomed, hemispherical in side view and made up of sand
    grains or small pieces of gravel, often temporarily sewn into place on a
    stone in a stream. Can be very abundant (Fig. 17) . . .   family Rhyacophilidae

—   Case never hemispherical in side view, rarely flat-bottomed 23

23 Case tubular, made of sand grains with a row of larger stones down each
    side (Fig. 18) . . . .   family Sericostomatidae

—   Case not as above . . . .
    Many families key out here
                —a good character has not been found to differentiate between them

Glossary

Abdomen—posterior section of the body, which is traditionally divided into head, thorax and abdomen.

Animalcule—the microscopic individuals of some colonial invertebrates which are anatomically fused together.

Antenna [plural Antennae]—"feeler": sensory appendage on the head of many invertebrates usually in the form of a long thin, segmented filament.

Beak—this refers to the specialised piercing mouthparts developed by most families of bugs; it is used to make holes in plant or animal prey so that fluids (often pre-digested by secreted enzymes) can be sucked into the bug's stomach.

Byssus—threads secreted by the mussel *Dreissena polymorpha* to attach itself to the substrate.

Carapace—a skeletal plate covering the thorax (and sometimes the abdomen) of some Crustacea: formed by the fusion of dorsal plates on the segments concerned.

Case—tubular construction of debris, cemented together by silk, made by some invertebrates (notably caddis larvae) to provide camouflage and protection: this is portable—when the animal moves it takes its case with it.

Chelae—the pincers of crabs and lobsters.

Chrysalis—immobile pupal stage of some insects.

Encrustation—a growth form of some colonial animals (e.g. sponges) whereby the substrate (stone or stick) is permanently overgrown.

Exoskeleton—the hardened "skin" of an arthropod used for rigidity against which the muscles can pull: growth is accomplished by shedding this periodically by moulting.

Eyespots—simple eyes found on some worms, flatworms and leeches. They give the animal very poor sight, but it can tell light from dark.

Filament—long thin "drawn-out" shape.

Gills—organs that abstract oxygen from the water and release accumulated carbon dioxide (breathing). They can take many forms: in primitive groups the whole body is a gill, some beetles use a bubble of air as a physical gill. Many animals have leaf-like plates or tufts of filaments on the abdomen or thorax which are used for this purpose.

Head capsule—the head of an insect with its hardened exoskeleton containing mouthparts, eyes, antennae etc.: particularly noticeable in those larvae which do not armour the thorax and abdomen, and are therefore soft-bodied and "worm-like" maggots.

Jointed legs—arthropod legs with true articulating joints.

Larva—juvenile stage of those insects which pupate (a stage which includes radical reorganisation of organs etc.) before the adult emerges.

Mask—a specialised mouthpart possessed by dragonfly and damselfly nymphs. It is a modified "lower lip", equipped with pseudo-jaws, which is jointed and can be shot out to capture prey.

Medusa—the free-swimming "jellyfish" stage in the Coelenterate life cycle.

Membranous—not hardened by skeletal materials.

Meniscus—the boundary to the "skin" of water around stones, dishes etc.

Nymph—juvenile stage of insects in which there is no pupal form; the adult emerges directly from the last nymphal skin. Characteristically, each successive nymphal stage increasingly resembles the adult, each possessing larger wing pads (in which the developing wings are housed) than the one before. The earliest stages do not have wing pads.

Operculum—a horny or calcified plate used by some snails to close off the aperture of the shell when they have retracted inside.

Palp—sensory appendage forming part of the mouthparts of some arthropods: usually takes the form of a short, segmented stalk or filament.

Polyp—"sea anemone" stage within the Coelenterate life cycle; usually attached to the substrate (cf. medusa).

Prolegs—soft, unjointed legs possessed by some invertebrates—may possess claws.

Pupa—stage in which the metamorphosis from larva to adult takes place in some insect groups. Often a passive stage (chrysalis), but in some groups (e.g. midges) the pupa remains active.

Puparium—the case which houses the pupa.

Segmentation—sub-division of the body into a number of similar units marked by segment junctions (e.g. earthworms, but also most higher forms).

Spiracles—pores through which air enters the breathing system of some insects.

Substrate—the floor of a stream or pool. [Latin *substratum*, pl. *substrata*]

Thorax—"middle" section of the arthropod body which is conventionally divided into head, thorax and abdomen.

Trachea—tubes through which air is transported around the body of insects.

Tube—silken construction of some invertebrates which is permanently attached to solid substrate or permanently immersed in mud: this is not portable.

Umbo—the point or origin of growth of a bivalve shell—as the shell gets bigger so the umbo gets surrounded by increments of shell material.

Valve—two of these make up the shell of a bivalve mollusc, they are mirror-images.

Wing cases—the hardened first pair of wings of some beetles and bugs which have been modified to protect the second, membranous, pair which are used for flying.

Wing pads—found on the thorax of insect nymphs, they enclose the developing wings.

NOTES

NOTES

NOTES

NOTES

NOTES

NOTES

AIDGAP PUBLICATIONS

The Field Studies Council (FSC) will have published eleven AIDGAP keys by the end of 1986:—

Hiscock, Sue (1979). *A field key to the British brown seaweeds* (FSC Publication 125).

Sykes, J. B. (1981). *An illustrated guide to the diatoms of British coastal plankton* (FSC Publication 140).

Unwin, D. M. (1981). *A key to families of British Diptera* (FSC Publication 143).

Crothers, John & Marilyn (1983). *A key to the crabs and crab-like animals of British inshore waters* (FSC Publication 155).

Cameron, R. A. D., Eversham, B. & Jackson, N. (1983). *A field guide to the slugs of the British Isles* (FSC Publication 156).

Unwin, D. M. (1984). *A key to the families of British Coleoptera (beetles) and Strepsiptera* (FSC Publication 166).

Willmer, Pat (1985). *Bees, ants and wasps—the British Aculeates* (FSC Occasional Publication 7).

Pankhurst, R. J. and Allinson, J. (1985). *British Grasses: a punched-card key to grasses in the vegetative state* (FSC Occasional Publication 10).

King, P. (1986). *Sea Spiders: a revised key to the adults of littoral pycnogonida of the British Isles* (FSC Publication 180).

Croft, P. (1986). *A key to the major Groups of British Freshwater Invertebrates* (FSC Publication 181).

Hiscock, Sue. (1986). *A field guide to the British Red Seaweeds* (FSC Occasional Publication 13).

Another key was published before the AIDGAP project was initiated, but it has been fully tested and revised:—

Haslam, S. M., Sinker, C. A. & Wolseley, P. A. (1975). *British Water Plants* (FSC Publication 107).

These, and many other titles, may be purchased when visiting Field Studies Council Centres or may be ordered through the post from:—

"Field Studies", Nettlecombe Court, Williton, Taunton, Somerset TA4 4HT,
or from

The Richmond Publishing Company Ltd., Orchard Road, Richmond,
Surrey TW9 4PD

A complete list of titles and prices is available from either of these addresses.